Bible Heroes

Adventures of
Great Men and Women of God

Arthur S. Maxwell

REVIEW AND HERALD®
PUBLISHING ASSOCIATION
HAGERSTOWN, MD 21740

Unless otherwise noted, all Bible verses are from the *Holy Bible*,
New International Version. Copyright © 1973, 1978, 1984, International
Bible Society. Used by permission of Zondervan Bible Publishers.

Bible texts credited to TEV are from the Good News Bible—Old
Testament: Copyright © American Bible Society 1976; New Testament:
Copyright © American Bible Society 1996, 1971, 1976.

Cover Illustration: Harry Anderson

PRINTED IN U.S.A.

06   7 6

R&H Cataloging Service
Maxwell, Arthur Stanley, 1896-1970.
    Bible heroes: adventures of great men and
women of God.

    1. Bible stories, English.   I. Title.

        220.9505

ISBN 0-8280-1040-4

CONTENTS

4

Fairest Creature of Creation

(Genesis 1:31; 2:18, 20-23)

A S ADAM watches the animals lying in the warm sunshine or playing happily in the meadows, he soon notices that they are in pairs. Every animal has a mate. Beside the majestic lion strides a sleek and slender lioness. Behind the antlered stag moves a graceful doe. With the powerful bull is a gentle cow. Near the tiger is a tigress. Close to the bear is a she-bear. Not far from Mr. Rabbit is Mrs. Rabbit, and it is so with the giraffes and zebras, the rhinos and the antelopes, the opossums and the squirrels. Only Adam is alone.

Of course, the animals are as friendly to him as they can be. When he calls to them they stop and look at him with their great, big, wondering eyes, but they cannot say a word in return. The little dog seems to understand him best, and it is clear that it wants ever so badly to speak. But all it can do is wiggle and jump about and bark and wag its tail.

Many times Adam must have wondered why he had no mate. Perhaps he began to search for one. Perhaps, out of the

Like a great master artist, God put the finishing touch on creation by making a woman, the world's first mother, the most lovely of all His creatures, whom Adam named Eve.

ache in his heart, he called and called, hoping that someone like him might hear his voice and answer. Perhaps he half expected to see some beautiful creature walking through the forest toward him to be his special friend and companion. But no one came.

As he lies on the grass and thinks about these things, he grows more and more lonely. The earth is so beautiful, the animals *so* friendly and amusing, but he has nobody to talk to, nobody with whom he can share his thoughts. Nobody, that is, except God.

Suddenly Adam begins to feel very sleepy. *This is strange*, he thinks. He has never felt like this before. What can be happening to him? He tries to stay awake, but it is no use. Moment by moment he becomes sleepier and sleepier, until at last he can keep his eyes open no longer. The earth, the flowers, the trees, the animals—all fade away and are forgotten as he falls into deep slumber.

Now God draws near to him, as near as He had been a little while before when He had breathed into his nostrils the breath of life. With one swift touch of His gentle, creative hands He removes a rib from the sleeping form before Him, closing up the wound with infinite skill.

"Then the Lord God made a woman from the rib he had taken out of the man."

What a strange thing for God to do! He made the sun, the moon, the stars, by saying, "Let there be lights in the expanse of the sky." He made all the fish and birds by saying, "Let the water teem with living creatures, and let birds fly above the earth across the expanse of the sky." Why didn't He say, "Let there be a woman"? And why, after making Adam, the most marvelous creature in His wonderful world, did He take a rib from his perfect body to make his life companion?

God must have had a good reason for acting this way. I like to think it was because He wanted Adam to know that his wife was truly part of him, so that he would always treat her as he would himself. The Bible tell us that God made Eve to be "a helper suitable for" Adam. Our word "helpmate" comes from this idea, and what a lovely thought it is! Eve was to stand by his side, always helping him, working with him, planning with him, and sharing life's joys with him.

Let us watch God at work again. Of Adam's rib we are told He "made" a woman. Even as He "formed" man of the dust of the ground, so now, with infinite wisdom and skill, He fashions the one who is to become the mother of the whole human race. How perfectly He molds the features of her lovely face! How gracefully He arranges her long, flowing hair! With what loving thought He places within her mind and heart all the tender-ness, all the gentleness, all the sweetness, all the endless store of love He wants every woman to have!

In less time than it takes to tell the fairest creature of all Creation stands before her Creator. Her eyes sparkle with the joy of life, and a tender smile gives her pretty face a beauty beyond compare. Now, slowly and gracefully, she takes her first few steps as God brings her "to the man." Wonderingly she looks down at the sleeping figure before her. Who can this be?

Dreaming perhaps of the companion he hopes to meet someday, somewhere, in this wonderful world God has given him, Adam stirs and opens his eyes. Oh, wonder of wonders! There before him stands someone more beautiful than he had dared to hope for. A being so special, so noble, so altogether lovely that he can scarcely believe that she is real.

Looking into her bright, kind, understanding eyes, he knows at once that this is his mate. This is the dear companion for whom he has longed. "The man said, 'This is now bone of my bones and flesh of my flesh; she shall be called "woman," for she was taken out of man.' "

It is love at first sight. Instantly both seem to know that they belong to each other. Eagerly they link hands and walk away together. As king and queen of the glorious new earth, they wander through the flower-filled fields, over the tree-studded hills, and down by the wave-swept shore. Together they explore the wonders of God's Creation and marvel at the glory of His power.

Meanwhile, not far away, silently watching over them in tender love, smiling at their perfect happiness, is God Himself. His joy is complete in theirs.

God's Shipbuilder

(Genesis 6:9-17, 22)

A S GOD began to look for someone to tell the people about His plans He thought of Noah. About 600 years old, Noah was a man whom God could trust with this task.

Keen, alert, and vigorous, he was one of the wisest men of his day. Though evil was all around him, he remained loyal to God and to what is right. The Bible says, "Noah was a righteous man, blameless among the people of his time, and he walked with God." Like Enoch, Noah stayed close to God. No doubt this is why God chose him for this most important job of warning the people about the Flood that would soon come.

Most likely Noah was a farmer, "a man of the soil." Certainly he was a skilled builder, or he never could have carried out God's instructions for making the ark. By this time people surely had boats of many kinds on their beautiful lakes and rivers.

One day—one of the great days in history—God came to Noah and said, "I am going to put an end to all people, for the earth is filled with violence because of them. . . . I am going to bring floodwaters on the earth to destroy all life under the heavens, every creature that has the breath of life in it. Everything on earth will perish."

The news must have saddened Noah. He knew that the people around him were very wicked and that they needed to be punished. But for God to destroy everybody and the whole beautiful world—that was something too dreadful to think about.

Even as God talked of punishment, He also told of a way out. Anyone who wanted to could follow God's plan and escape from the Flood.

"Make yourself an ark of cypress wood," God said.

An ark! That meant something that would float. We would call it a ship. But would it be large enough to hold all the people who might want to find safety from the Flood in it?

Noah must have been amazed at the figures God gave him. It was no small lifeboat that God had in mind, but a huge vessel. It was to be 515 feet (157 meters) long, 86 feet (26 meters) wide, and 52 feet (16 meters) high. That's longer than a football field, and about half as wide.

Why did God ask Noah to build so large a ship? First, He wanted all to know that the ship had room for them if they

wished to be saved. Second, He planned to rescue many birds and animals in it. And third, He knew it would have to ride out the worst storms and the roughest seas of all time.

After Noah was alone again, he must have thought for a long time about what God had asked him to do. What a lot of trees would have to be cut down and hauled to the building site! Imagine all the sawing, planing, and shaping that would have to be done. And all the men who would have to be hired—and paid! It was a huge task for anyone to tackle.

Noah also must have wondered what everybody would think when they saw him building a ship more than 500 feet (152 meters) long! Most likely they would say he was out of his mind, throwing his money away on a crazy idea. But "Noah did everything just as God commanded him." People do just that, regardless of what others may think of them, when they are walking with God.

So Noah started to work, drawing the plans, preparing the lumber, and laying the keel.

At first the neighbors probably didn't take much notice. But as the years went by, and one by one the great wooden ribs of the vessel were fastened in place, it became clear that Noah was building a ship and not a barn.

Noah's neighbors began to make fun of him. How they laughed! They could see no reason for building anything like

this. What would anybody want with a boat this big? They probably felt quite sure it wouldn't float anyway, even if Noah could get it into the water.

Noah tried to explain, but it was no use. As people flocked to watch him work he warned them of the Flood that was coming and explained that God had told him to build a place of safety for those who wanted it.

The more he tried to explain, however, the more they made fun of him. But he went on building and preaching just the same. And the years, the last few years of that beautiful world, slipped away.

The Animals Move In

(Genesis 7:1-16)

ONE HUNDRED and twenty years had gone by since Noah started to build the ark. The great ship was finished. Fifty-two feet (16 meters) high and more than 515 feet (157 meters) long, it had become a landmark, visible for miles in every direction.

Everybody knew about it, but they all had become so used to it they didn't even bother to go near it anymore. They only pointed at it with a smile and said, "Noah's folly!"

The vast ship looked barren and deserted, for only Noah and his family remained. All the hired workmen had left. They worked for their pay, and now that the job was over they had gone home. They never really believed Noah's message.

The great door of the ark stood open, as if inviting everybody to enter and find safety, but nobody came. There was a strange silence everywhere, broken only by the sound of echoing feet as Noah and his sons walked through the empty vessel, making sure everything was firm and strong and watertight.

For 120 years the old man had preached of coming destruc-

tion, but nowhere was
as peaceful as here. Not even the sound of a
saw or a hammer was heard. Could Noah have
made a mistake? Could he have misunderstood what God
had said to him? Perhaps nothing would happen after all. Perhaps he had wasted his time and money. Perhaps the ark would
just rot away where it stood.

But look! Something *is* happening! See! Those animals
over there! They seem to be walking toward the ark. They are.
Now others are coming from all directions. What can it mean?

People ran to see the amazing sight. Animals of every kind
made their way to the ark, as if guided by some invisible hand.

Great elephants lumbered up the creaking timbers of the
ramp and through the open door. Behind them were growling
tigers, grunting bears, and bleating sheep, followed by zebras,
antelopes, kangaroos, pandas, donkeys, goats, and a host of
others. Squirrels, opossums, beavers, chipmunks, and all sorts
of little creatures scurried along in between.

What a sight! Nothing like it had ever happened before. Yet even now the people who were looking on in astonishment did not understand. They thought it was all very funny. Noah, they said, had decided to turn his ark into a zoo, since he couldn't get it to float.

As the last of the animals passed through the door, Noah came to the side of the ark and made a final plea to the people to follow them in.

"There's going to be a great flood!" he cried. "The whole world is about to be destroyed. That is why the animals have come.

They understand. Come! Come, before it is forever too late!"

Still no one took a step toward the ark. They just laughed as they had done before. "Go live with your animals," they sneered as they returned to their homes and their sins.

Now God spoke to Noah again. "Go into the ark, you and your whole family, because I have found you righteous in this generation. Take with you seven of every kind of clean animal, a male and its mate, and two of every kind of unclean animal, a male and its mate, and also seven of every kind of bird, male and female, to keep their various kinds alive throughout the earth. Seven days from now I will send rain on the earth for forty days and forty nights, and I will wipe from the face of the earth every living creature I have made."

Nothing more could have been done. The people had had their opportunity. They had been given their warning. But they didn't care. Blinded by sin, self-satisfied, and set in their evil ways, they didn't want to be saved. Their ears were deaf to God's message.

So Noah left them. The Bible says, "On that very day Noah and his sons, Shem, Ham and Japheth, together with his wife and the wives of his three sons, entered the ark. . . . The animals going in were male and female of every living thing, as God had commanded Noah. Then the Lord shut him in."

As the great door closed silently and mysteriously, shut by an unseen hand, Noah caught one last glimpse of the beautiful world outside—a world he would never see again.

Heaven's Floodgates Open

(Genesis 7:10-20)

INSIDE the ark Noah waited and wondered. For seven long days his faith was tested. Had he done right? Had he preached the truth? Would the Flood really happen as he had predicted?

Outside, some of the people began to wonder too. The shut door bothered them. Perhaps they should have listened to Noah and gone in. Maybe the old man was right, after all. But since nothing happened, they soon got over their fears and smiled again at the thought of Noah and his family inside there with all those animals.

The days passed by. The last days of the world. Three, four, five, six.

The morning of the seventh day dawned, but instead of brilliant sunshine, black, angry clouds covered the sky. Lightning flashed. Thunder roared. Drops of water began to fall. It was raining for the first time in the history of the world. Water from the sky! Just as Noah had said would happen! The preacher was right, after all.

The heavy downpour increased every minute. Water began to pour off the roofs of houses and rushed down the roadways. Streams filled up and overflowed their banks. Low-lying land became swampy. Small lakes formed everywhere.

Water poured all over the place. Streets, basements, lower floors of houses, were all flooded. People began to rush upstairs onto their roofs. Some looked toward the ark and wished they had gone inside while the door had been still open. Others left their homes and hurried to higher ground, but the water followed them.

"It is the Flood!" they cried. "Noah's Flood is upon us!"

But worse was to come. Look over there! A wall of water was rushing in from the sea. A tidal wave!

Everyone ran for dear life. People climbed trees and rushed

frantically up hillsides, but still the water rose higher and higher.

There was no escape, because "on that day all the springs of the great deep burst forth, and the floodgates of the heavens were opened."

Some tried to scramble up the steep sides of the ark. They battered frantically at the door. "Open!" they cried. "Open the door! Let us in! We are sorry for our sins!" But it was too late to be sorry now.

Swiftly the water rose, rose, rose. Houses were washed away. Forests disappeared. Hills became islands, then vanished beneath the waves.

Panic-stricken people clung desperately to the last high rocks. First one, then another, lost their grip and plunged into the raging seas. Higher and ever higher rose the water until finally it covered all the hills and mountains.

Meanwhile, the wind-lashed tide surged around the ark, beating on it, tugging at it, splashing over it. The mighty ship rolled, heaved, lifted. It was off with its precious cargo!

The Strangest Voyage in History

(Genesis 7:17-8:14)

CAUGHT up on the raging waters, the ark was swept forward by fierce tides and howling gales on the strangest voyage in history.

Only a strong, well-built ship could have taken the stresses and strains of those first few days and nights. With awful earthquakes, "all the springs of the great deep" were broken up, and "the floodgates of the heavens" rained down their deadly flood of water.

The ark had nowhere to go—no harbor anywhere. "All the high mountains under the entire heavens were covered." So it just drifted this way and that, rolling and tossing as the terrific currents were coming and going.

Rising to meet one giant wave, it would plunge down again into the trough on the other side, only to meet another towering whitecap rushing toward it. Again and again it must have been struck by huge walls of water that swept over it from stem to stern. Floating trees and logs were always a danger. But because God was protecting it, the ark didn't capsize and sink.

The violent movement and lack of light and fresh air made life in the ark hard to bear. Worst of all, Noah and his family couldn't help wondering how it would all end.

Big as the ark was, Noah and his family were the only human passengers. The boat had room for hundreds more, but no one else chose to come aboard. Now all those who had refused to come were drowned. Everybody. Men and women, boys and girls. The old world had completely disappeared beneath billions of tons of water.

"Every living thing that moved on the earth perished. . . . Men and animals and the creatures that move along the ground and the birds of the air were wiped from the earth. Only Noah was left, and those with him in the ark."

How God must have watched over the ark through this whole fearful experience! Did you ever stop to think how much it meant to Him? All His hopes and plans for the world depended on that handful of people inside. His promises could come true only through them. Only through somebody in that storm-tossed ship could Eve's Offspring ever crush the snake's head.

How Satan must have tried to sink the ark in the terrible storm! If the ark had been lost, God's plan would have failed. But the ark did not sink. Under God's care, it rode out the storm.

"But God remembered Noah and all the wild animals and the livestock that were with him in the ark. . . . And the rain had stopped falling from the sky. . . . The ark came to rest on the mountains of Ararat."

Yet even after the ark had touched ground, Noah and his family couldn't see any land—only water, water, everywhere.

When Noah noticed the increasing stillness and that the

big waves were no longer hitting the sides of the ark, he knew that the worst of the Flood was over and that the water was going down. "The waters continued to recede until the tenth month, and on the first day of the tenth month the tops of the mountains became visible."

What a day that was, and what a shout must have gone up from all eight of them at the welcome sight! "Land! Land!" they must have cried, with the joy of those who have been long at sea.

Now "Noah opened the window he had made in the ark" and let out two birds, first a raven, then a dove. The raven flew off happily, but the dove returned. Noah decided to wait a week and see how far the water would go down by then.

At the end of the week he let the dove go again. This time it came back with an olive leaf in its beak. Everyone was cheered at this, for it showed that the waters were still going down.

Noah waited another week and sent the dove out once more. This time it did not come back, and Noah felt sure the land was drying up. So he "removed the covering from the ark and saw that the surface of the ground was dry."

The rain had stopped, and the sun was breaking through the clouds. The Flood was over. The strangest voyage in history had ended in the strangest way you could imagine. The ark was resting on a mountaintop in Asia Minor.

Beginning Again

(Genesis 8:15-22; 9:1-17)

AT LAST came the big moment everyone in the ark had been waiting for—the opening of the great door that God had closed.

Maybe Noah and his three sons tried to roll it back. Finally it creaked open, perhaps moved by the same mighty hand that had closed it. How glad everyone must have been to step outside and breathe the sweet, fresh air again!

Noah was so thankful God had saved him and his family from the Flood that he built an altar as soon as he left the ark. He sacrificed at least one of "all the clean animals and clean birds." That was a real sacrifice just then, when the only animals in the whole world were those that had been with him in the ark.

God was very pleased that Noah had remembered to say Thank You for his deliverance. He told him, "Never again will I curse the ground because of man. . . . As long as the earth endures, seedtime and harvest, cold and heat, summer and winter, day and night will never cease."

Now, at God's command, all the birds and beasts were released. What a sight that must have been! What a whirring of wings, as great eagles, storks, herons, and flamingoes burst into the air and flew to freedom! Robins, sparrows, thrushes, and warblers fluttered and hopped along behind them.

How the nightingales trilled and the blackbirds squawked! The mockingbirds must have tried to sing everybody's song at once in that joyful moment of freedom!

Lions and tigers, buffaloes and hippos, elephants and giraffes, sheep and goats, dogs and cats, hurried through the great doorway, jostling one another as they bounded down the ramp in their eagerness to get out into the open again.

What a noise they must have made as they sounded forth their joy, the lions roaring, the elephants trumpeting, the horses neighing, the oxen lowing, the donkeys braying, and all the little dogs barking their loudest!

Many of the animals disappeared at once, racing down the mountainside until they were out of sight. Perhaps others stayed around because they liked being close to people. Noah must have wondered what he would do with so many if they continued to stay near the ark, but two by two, and group by group, the animals began to move away. They wandered north, south, east, and west, looking for food and shelter. At last only some cows, sheep, goats, and of course little dogs and cats, were left.

Meanwhile Noah and his family looked around at the wild-looking place to which the ark had brought them. It was a sad sight. Everywhere they could see the wreckage and

ruin caused by the raging waters. Great trees lay uprooted. Lovely hills had been swept clean of soil, leaving nothing but bare rock. Mountains had become scarred and jagged. Plains that had been so fruitful were deserts now.

Not a single human dwelling was left anywhere. Not a trace remained of the beautiful homes they remembered. Everything had been smashed to small pieces by the towering tidal waves that had swept the earth when the Flood began. The desolation was enough to break their hearts.

As they stood there viewing the desolate scene they felt the earth tremble under them. Many earthquakes shook the ground, as the earth settled after the great eruptions when "all the springs of the great deep . . . were opened." How afraid and lonely they felt on that shuddering mountainside. They must have wondered what terrible thing was going to happen next.

Suddenly Noah looked up. In the sky he saw something he had never seen before. A glorious arch of many colors was glowing in the sky. It seemed to circle the ruined earth with arms of love.

Hardly daring to breathe, they stood looking at it, unable to speak. What was it? What could it mean?

As they watched in wonder, God drew near and said, "I have set my rainbow in the clouds, and it will be the sign of the covenant between me and the earth. Whenever I bring clouds

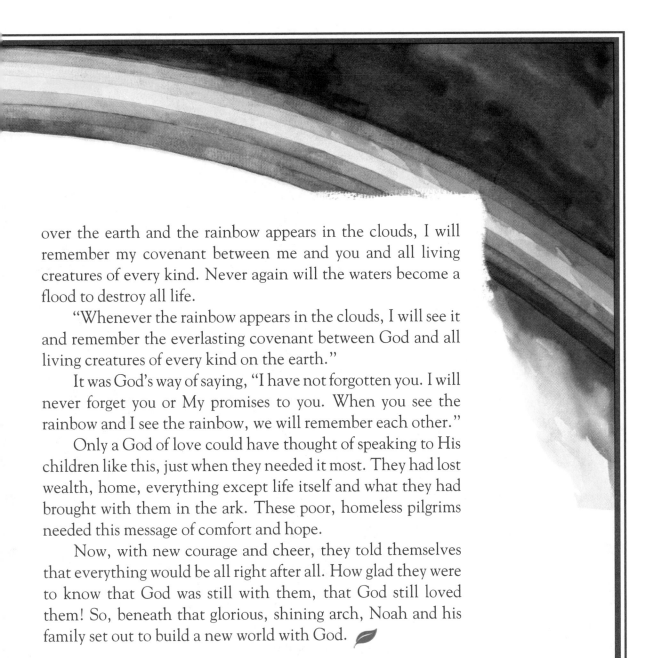

over the earth and the rainbow appears in the clouds, I will remember my covenant between me and you and all living creatures of every kind. Never again will the waters become a flood to destroy all life.

"Whenever the rainbow appears in the clouds, I will see it and remember the everlasting covenant between God and all living creatures of every kind on the earth."

It was God's way of saying, "I have not forgotten you. I will never forget you or My promises to you. When you see the rainbow and I see the rainbow, we will remember each other."

Only a God of love could have thought of speaking to His children like this, just when they needed it most. They had lost wealth, home, everything except life itself and what they had brought with them in the ark. These poor, homeless pilgrims needed this message of comfort and hope.

Now, with new courage and cheer, they told themselves that everything would be all right after all. How glad they were to know that God was still with them, that God still loved them! So, beneath that glorious, shining arch, Noah and his family set out to build a new world with God.

Baby to the Rescue

(Exodus 1:15-2:10)

AS PHARAOH rode out in his chariot one day to inspect his two new treasure cities, Pithom and Rameses, he saw something that worried him at first, then made him angry.

He had never seen so many Hebrews in all his life. They were in the fields and all around the brick ovens. They were unloading blocks of stone from barges on the river and hauling other blocks into place on the houses and temples they were building. They were everywhere.

Worst of all, every one of them looked so strong and healthy! He had thought he would kill them off with hard labor, but now there were more of them than ever. His plan had not worked.

Pharaoh decided that if he could not get rid of the Hebrews by working them to death, he would do it some other way. What could be easier than killing their infants as soon as they were born? So Pharaoh decreed that every

Pharaoh's daughter was surprised to see the baby lying inside the basket. She lovingly smiled and cooed at him to stop his crying.

baby boy must be thrown into the Nile River.

When the Hebrew fathers and mothers heard the dreadful news, their faces turned pale. At first they could hardly believe it. No ruler could be so cruel as to order that all baby boys should be murdered like this!

But it *was* true. Soon terror filled the hearts of all as they heard stories about Egyptians taking babies away from their mothers and flinging them into the Nile to drown or be eaten by crocodiles. Imagine how the people must have felt in homes where a baby was on the way or had just arrived! Imagine how the older brothers and sisters must have worried themselves sick, to say nothing of the fathers and mothers.

This was Israel's darkest hour. They had put up with the long hours of work and the merciless acts of the slave masters, but this cold-blooded killing of their children was too much to bear. It made them want to leave Egypt more than ever. They began to pray for help as they had never prayed before, and they wanted it *now*.

At this very moment, when things seemed as though they could not get worse, God sent a baby to the rescue.

It happened this way. One day a baby boy was born to Amram and Jochebed. These godly Hebrews had a little girl called Miriam and a little boy named Aaron, and they had wanted another little boy so much. But now! Oh, dear! What if the soldiers should find him?

Nobody knows for sure what name the parents gave their new baby. Maybe it was Abraham or Enoch or Joseph. Whatever it was, it became lost. Later on, as we shall see, he was given another name, and this one stuck to him for life.

Jochebed was a loving mother, and she made up her mind that the Egyptians would not get her baby, not if she could help it. Somehow or other she managed to keep him hidden for three months, but it's pretty hard to hide 3-month-old babies anywhere. Just think of the noise they make when they cry!

One day, when Jochebed knew she could not keep her secret any longer, she got a bright idea. She would make a little boat, put the baby in it, and float it near the riverbank. Perhaps—who could tell?—some kindhearted Egyptian woman passing by might find it and feel sorry for the poor little thing inside.

Jochebed took a desperate chance, but it seemed to be the only way out. It was better than doing nothing. Any moment someone might burst into the house and snatch away her baby.

Jochebed wove a basket with reeds from the river, making

it watertight by coating it with tar. Then she fixed a soft little bed inside and tenderly—oh, so tenderly!—laid her baby in it. She kissed him goodbye, closed the lid, and carried the basket to the riverbank.

With a breaking heart and tears running down her cheeks, she placed it gently among the marsh plants. Then, leaving Miriam to watch what would happen, she went home and asked God to protect her child.

Miriam was not alone on that riverbank. Angels were there, too, watching with her. This was a special baby for whom God had planned a very wonderful future.

After a while, who should walk by but Pharaoh's daughter, with some of her maids. Suddenly she caught sight of the strange oblong basket in the rushes, and sent one of her maids to carry it to her. Lifting the lid, the princess saw a beautiful baby boy inside, and the poor little thing was crying.

"This is one of the Hebrew babies," she said. Perhaps she

picked him up and loved him. The Bible says she "felt sorry for him." At least she wasn't cruel and hardhearted like her father.

As her maids crowded around to look at the baby, wondering what to do with him, Miriam came running up. It must have taken a lot of courage for her to speak to the princess, but with her baby brother's life in danger, she was ready to do anything.

"Please, ma'am," she said, "shall I go and get one of the Hebrew women to nurse the baby for you?"

Pharaoh's daughter was relieved. This seemed to be a good way out of a very awkward situation. "Yes, go," she said. So Miriam ran like the wind to find her mother.

"Mother, Mother!" I can hear her gasping as she rushed into the house. "Come quickly, come quickly! The princess has found baby brother!"

How long do you suppose it took Jochebed to get from her house to the riverbank? Not very long. She had never run so

fast in her life. When she saw the princess and her maids and the baby crying for his dinner, she was so happy she didn't know whether to laugh or to cry. Of course, she tried to keep a straight face so the princess wouldn't think that she was the child's mother.

Then the princess spoke to her, and she could hardly believe her ears. "Take this baby," she said gently, "and nurse him for me, and I will pay you."

The way Jochebed took the baby and cuddled it was enough to give her away, but if the princess guessed the truth, she didn't say anything. As she left with her maids for the palace, Jochebed and Miriam hurried happily home. Their hearts were overflowing with thankfulness to God for the way He had saved their precious little boy.

It was all too wonderful to believe. Not only did they have their baby back, but no one could ever kill him now. He belonged to the princess, and she was going to pay his own mother to take care of him! She could give him the best food, the best care, and Pharaoh's daughter would pay for it!

If the princess had known who this child would be someday and what he would do, would she have saved his life? I don't know. Perhaps she would have. This baby was the very one God had sent to lead His people out of Egypt to freedom.

Training a Prince

(Exodus 2:10; Acts 7:20-23)

JOCHEBED was glad to have her baby back safe and sound. As she thought over what had happened down by the river, she realized that her baby didn't really belong to her anymore. Her own little baby had a new mother. Someday the princess would send for him, and take him away, and never give him back again. He would not grow up to be Jochebed's child, a Hebrew; he would be a prince of Egypt.

"How long will I be able to keep him?" she must have asked herself again and again. One year, two years, 10 years? She didn't know. But she made up her mind that during the time she was allowed to keep him, whether it was long or short, she would give him the very best training she could.

Jochebed knew that her son would meet many temptations in the palace, so she tried to anchor his little heart to God. She taught him to pray and to sing songs of praise. She told him the story of Creation and the Fall. She talked about God's plan of salvation, that sweet and beautiful story that had been handed down from parent to child from the days of Adam and Eve.

God, she taught him, is a holy God who expects all His children to be good and pure and loyal. Those who want to be truly happy will follow His teachings and obey His laws. She told him about the history of his people and how God had promised Abraham that someday they would all be delivered from slavery and taken back to Canaan. She also told him about his own wonderful rescue from death and that she believed God had a wonderful plan for his life if he stayed true and loyal to Him.

All too quickly the years went by. Then one day, when her boy was 12 years old, the dreaded message arrived. The princess wanted her son brought to the palace at once.

What a sad day! Mother choked back her sobs as she packed up the few things he would need to take along with him. Father blinked back his tears. Miriam cried her heart out. Aaron looked glum, not sure whether to be sad or envious.

Perhaps some soldiers came in a chariot to get him. I don't know. Maybe the family walked to the palace and stood together outside before the gates swung open. The boy's heart would have been full of questioning, and the parents' hearts would have been full of fears and sadness. Then came the last goodbyes, the last promises to remember and love forever.

When the guards took the youngster inside and the gates closed behind him, the great palace must have seemed to be a

very lonely place to him. His new mother must have tried to be especially kind to him, but somehow it wasn't the same. The princess also gave him a new name. She said it would be Moses, which meant "son" in Egyptian and "drawn out" in the Hebrew language. Perhaps Moses cried himself to sleep that night, thinking that he would never return to his home and dear ones again.

But with the morning came new interests. Everywhere Moses turned he saw wonderful things. Life here was so different from everything he had known in the humble little cottage that had been his home until now.

The Bible tells us that he was "no ordinary child," and he was soon a favorite in the court. Everybody loved him. The best teachers in the country tutored him in mathematics, law, medicine, military science, and many other things. As time went by, Moses became "educated in all the wisdom of the Egyptians and was powerful in speech and action."

Moses soon reached the prime of life. His body was strong, and his mind was keen. He already had the qualities of a great leader. He could ride a horse or drive a chariot with skill and daring. He had learned his lessons so well that he knew a lot about the history, geography, and religion of Egypt.

All the court—in fact, all Egypt—knew that here was a young man of unusual gifts who would be able to take Pharaoh's place someday. And Moses himself was aware that he was in

direct line to the throne. Someday, if he wanted to, he could become ruler of Egypt.

Yet with all his studies and busy life in the royal court, Moses never forgot the things his mother had told him in his boyhood. Every day he thought about God and what Mother had said God wanted him to be and to do. As the years slipped by he felt more and more out of place in the palace. Deep loyalties, which court life could not change, drew him toward his people.

The Hebrews were suffering more all the time. Moses heard reports of the terrible way the Hebrew slaves were being treated, and he often wondered how he could help them. If he revealed that he was not an Egyptian after all, but belonged to the very people the Egyptians despised, he would lose his position and his chance for the throne. What should he do?

When Moses said his prayers, he talked with God about it all, asking Him to make clear what he should do. Then one night he made his decision—"He chose to be mistreated along with the people of God rather than to enjoy the pleasures of sin for a short time. He regarded disgrace for the sake of Christ as of greater value than the treasures of Egypt." *

It was a big choice to make, and it proved to be a turning point in the history of Israel and of the world.

_____
* Hebrews 11:25, 26.

The Strongest Man
Who Ever Lived

(Judges 14-16)

SAMSON became the strongest man who ever lived. Thanks to the loving care his parents gave him, he grew to be so big and strong that nobody could overpower him. Once, when he was still quite young, he tore a lion apart with his bare hands.

But though his body was strong, he was selfish and headstrong and a great problem to his father and mother.

As Samson was growing up he fell in love with a Philistine girl and wanted to marry her right away. Naturally his parents tried to persuade him not to do such a thing. "Can't you find a nice Israelite girl to marry?" they said to him, kindly but earnestly. "Why do you want a wife from our enemies?"

But Samson wouldn't listen to them. "Get her for me," he said. "She's the right one for me." So he married her. And what a lot of trouble and sorrow that marriage brought to them all.

One day as Samson happened to pass the carcass of a lion he had killed, he noticed that there was a swarm of bees and honey in it. This gave him an idea for a bit of fun at his

wedding feast. Thirty young men were at the wedding as
guests, and he asked them the meaning of this riddle: "Out of
the eater, something to eat; out of the strong, something
sweet." Then he offered to give them each a suit of clothes
if they could give the answer during the seven days of the
feast. If they failed to answer in that time, they were to give
him 30 suits.

Unable to guess the riddle the young men began to get
worried. They were afraid they would all have to give their own
clothes to Samson, and then what would they do?

On the seventh day they came to Samson's wife and per-
suaded her to try to find out the meaning of the riddle. She
pleaded with Samson to tell her, and in a moment of weakness
he did. Then she told the young men, and they came to Samson
and said, "What is sweeter than honey? What is stronger than a
lion?"

Samson was so angry that his wife had told his secret that
he went and killed 30 Philistines and brought their clothes and
gave them to the 30 young men. Then—after being with his
wife only seven days—he left her in a huff and went back to his
old home.

When he had cooled down a bit, he decided to go back to
his wife, but he found that she had married someone else,

thinking he didn't love her anymore. This made Samson furious. To get even with the Philistines, he caught 300 foxes and tied them together in pairs, tail to tail, with a firebrand in between. Then he let the maddened animals loose in the grainfields and vineyards of the Philistines. You can imagine what happened. Those foxes must have set fire to hundreds of acres, leaving only blackened fields behind them.

Now it was the Philistines' turn to get angry. They marched into the land of Judah and demanded that Samson be handed over to them for punishment. So 3,000 men of Judah surrounded Samson, bound him, and gave him to the Philistines. But no sooner was he back among his enemies than he broke the ropes binding him as though they were "charred flax" and, picking up the jawbone of a donkey, slew a thousand men with it.

By this time Samson's fame as the strongest man on earth was spreading. Everybody was afraid of him. The Philistines couldn't catch him, however hard they tried. One night when he was in Gaza, the rulers of the city shut the gates so that he couldn't get away. But at midnight Samson carried away both gates and gateposts and dumped them on the top of a hill 38 miles (61 kilometers) away!

The next morning, when the Philistines saw that great gap in the walls of Gaza, they must have had a shock. But what could they do? This giant of a man was just too strong and too smart for them.

Then they heard that Samson had fallen in love with a woman named Delilah, and they made up their minds to work through her to get him. "Find the secret of his strength," they begged her. She tried to, but it wasn't easy. Three times Samson lied to her.

Once he told her that if she tied him up with seven fresh bowstrings, he would be helpless. But when she tied him up, he snapped them in a moment.

Another time he said that if she tied him with new strips of leather, he would be as weak as other men. But when she had gone to all the trouble of finding the leather and tying him up with them, he broke them as if they had been thread.

The third time he told her—for fun—that if she were to weave his hair in with the cloth she was making, he would never be able to get free. That night while he was asleep, she did that very thing. But in the morning he walked off with all the weaving machinery hanging from his head and laughed at her.

Day after day Delilah, pouting and fussing and teasing until "he was tired to death," asked Samson to tell her his secret. He just couldn't stand it any longer. Then he told her.

The secret of his strength, he said, lay in the fact that he was a Nazirite, a man dedicated to God. Because he was a Nazirite, his hair had never been cut, and it was done up in seven long locks. If they were ever cut off, he said, he would really become as weak as other men.

Feeling sure that he had told her the truth at last, Delilah planned to cut off his hair that very night, and she invited the lords of the Philistines to come up and see the result.

After Samson had fallen asleep, she had a man shave his head. The seven beautiful locks, the symbol of his devotion to God, fell to the floor, and his strength went with them.

"Samson, the Philistines are upon you!" she cried, but he couldn't do a thing about it. He tried to put up a fight, but "the Lord had left him."

Now he was made a prisoner. The Philistines put out his eyes, bound him with chains of bronze, and set him to work in a treadmill.

Poor Samson! What a miserable failure he had made of everything! It is hard to think that the blind, fettered man in the treadmill was once that little boy his parents had loved so dearly, the boy God had counted on to deliver Israel. How old Manoah and his wife must have wept over him and wished that somehow they might have stopped him from going with those heathen girls! But it was too late now.

As that treadmill went round and round and round, Samson had time to think of all his mistakes and the life he might

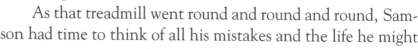

have lived. In shame and sorrow he turned back to God and pleaded for one more chance.

As week after week and month after month went by, he noticed that his hair was growing again. And every inch it grew seemed to bring him closer to God. Gradually he felt his old strength coming back.

Then one day he was let out of the treadmill. He heard people talking about a great feast to Dagon, god of the Philistines. Someone told him that he had been released so he could entertain the merrymakers.

He guessed where he was being taken. He had been to the place before and remembered that there were two big pillars in the center of the building that supported the roof. An idea came to him. He asked the lad who was leading him by the hand to show him where the pillars were, so he could lean on them.

When the boy brought him to the place, he cried from the depths of his soul, "O Sovereign Lord, remember me. O God, please strengthen me just once more, and let me with one blow

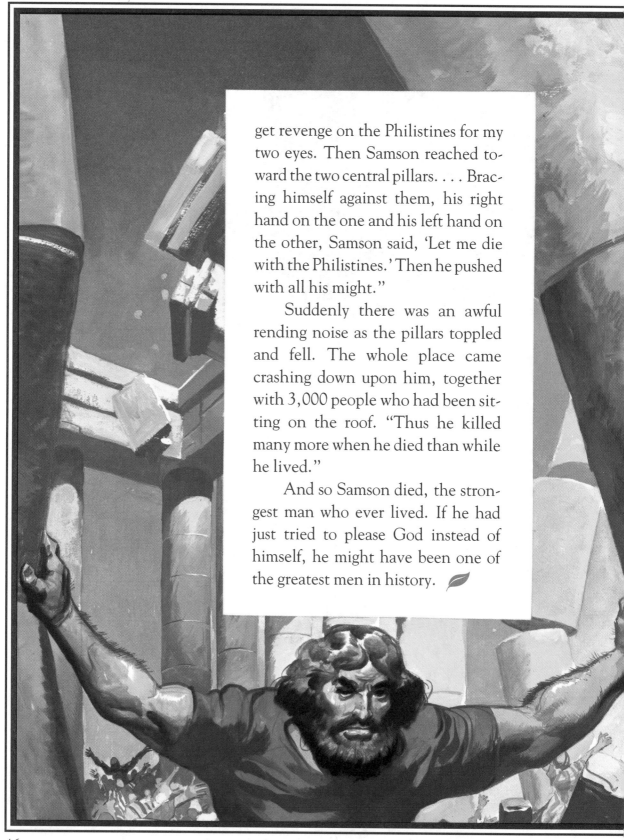

get revenge on the Philistines for my two eyes. Then Samson reached toward the two central pillars. . . . Bracing himself against them, his right hand on the one and his left hand on the other, Samson said, 'Let me die with the Philistines.' Then he pushed with all his might."

Suddenly there was an awful rending noise as the pillars toppled and fell. The whole place came crashing down upon him, together with 3,000 people who had been sitting on the roof. "Thus he killed many more when he died than while he lived."

And so Samson died, the strongest man who ever lived. If he had just tried to please God instead of himself, he might have been one of the greatest men in history.

Gleaner Girl

(Ruth 1-4)

OUT OF all the darkness and sadness of the days when Israel was ruled by the judges comes one of the sweetest stories ever told. It is about a girl called Ruth, who belonged to the Moabites, long-time enemies of Israel.

As a child, I suppose she heard only bad things about the Israelites, and if she hadn't met Naomi, maybe she never would have known any better. Naomi was the mother of two boys about Ruth's age. One was called Mahlon, the other, Kilion. Their father's name was Elimelech and the four of them had come all the way from Bethlehem to Moab because of a famine in their own country.

After Elimelech's death Ruth and Mahlon fell in love and married. Also a girl friend of Ruth's named Orpah, married Kilion. The five of them were very happy together, for Naomi was the nicest mother-in-law any girl could wish to have. She loved her daughters-in-law dearly, and they loved her just as much.

— PAINTING BY KREIGH COLLINS

God answered Samson's prayer and gave him strength to destroy the temple of the fish-god Dagon and three thousand Philistines who had mocked him and oppressed the people of Israel.

Naomi was a godly woman, and she must have been very sorry when her sons married heathen girls. But she made up her mind to lead them, if she could, to love the God of Israel. She took every chance to talk to them of God's love and to tell them the stories she had heard from her parents long before.

Naomi explained to Ruth and Orpah how God created the world in the beginning and made it into a beautiful home for man, how Adam and Eve sinned and lost their garden home, and how God planned to give it back to them some day. She also told them about the Flood and the rescue of Noah and his family in the ark, of God's promises to Abraham, the dark days in Egypt, the great deliverance in the days of Moses, and all God had done for His people since then.

Ruth and Orpah loved to listen as Naomi talked to them. They especially liked to hear of the wonderful things she believed God would do for Israel in the future. Naomi may have told them that someday, through some sweet girl, Eve's Offspring would come to crush the snake's head.

Ten years passed by. Then trouble came, and great sorrow. First Mahlon died, then Kilion, one after the other.

The sadness in that home must have been terrible. How Naomi, Ruth, and Orpah must have cried together. Poor things! It must have been hard for them to believe in the goodness of God. But they did.

Brave Naomi decided she would go back to her old home in Bethlehem, and the two girls said they would go with her. On the way, however, Naomi began to worry about them. She wondered whether she was doing right in taking them away from their own country. Perhaps they would be better off if they were to go back to their mothers.

"Go back, each of you, to your mother's home," she said to them kindly: "May the Lord show kindness to you, as you have shown to your dead and to me." Then she kissed them, and they all burst out crying again.

Both Ruth and Orpah said they would rather stay with her than go back to their homeland. They wouldn't leave her. They loved her too much. But Naomi said it was better for them to go back to their own homes. They must find new husbands, she said, and it would be easier to do this where they were known, among their own people.

They talked for a long time about it, and finally Orpah decided that maybe Naomi was right. She said goodbye with many tears and turned around to go back home. I can see her waving her last farewell before disappearing from view around a bend in the road.

But Ruth wouldn't go. In words that will live forever, she told Naomi, "Don't urge me to leave you. . . . Where you go I will go, and where you stay I will stay. Your people will be my

people and your God my God."

So Naomi and Ruth went on their way together, trudging slowly and sadly up the rough, steep mountain trail that led to Bethlehem. When they finally arrived at the village, everyone in town was excited. "Naomi is back!" the people cried, crowding around to hear the news she brought from the land of Moab.

"But where is your husband?" they asked. And, "Where are the boys?" Tearfully Naomi told her story. "I went away full, but the Lord has brought me back empty."

Fortunately the barley harvest was just beginning, so there was work to do and food to eat. Ruth offered to go into the fields and glean with the other village girls. In those days, grain was cut and gathered by hand, and what was left by the reapers could be picked up by the gleaners.

One day as she was busily at work, Boaz, the owner of the field, came by. Seeing a strange girl among his gleaners, he stopped to ask who she was.

The man in charge replied, "She is the Moabitess who came back from Moab with Naomi."

Boaz was interested. He had wanted to meet her, especially since Naomi was a relative of his. Calling Ruth to him, he told her he had heard about her kindness to Naomi and how she had willingly left her own country to come and live among strangers. "May the Lord repay you for what you have done. May you be richly rewarded by the Lord, the God of Israel, under whose wings you have come to take refuge," he said.

Smiling sweetly, Ruth thanked him for his kind words; and Boaz, liking her more every minute, told the reapers to let some of the sheaves drop where she could glean them. He wanted to make sure Ruth would have lots of grain to take home to Naomi.

As the days went by, Boaz and Ruth saw more and more of each other, and one day there was a wedding in Bethlehem. It must have been quite an event, for Boaz was very rich and Ruth was very poor, and a Moabitess too.

People must have talked about it for weeks, and they would have talked even more if they had known what this marriage would mean in the years ahead. For Ruth and Boaz had a son called Obed. And Obed had a son called Jesse. And Jesse had a son called David.

So Ruth—dear, kind, faithful Ruth—was the great-grandmother of King David. She was a direct ancestor of Joseph the husband of Mary who, more than 1,000 years later, in this very same village of Bethlehem, gave birth to the baby Jesus.

I am sure Ruth never dreamed that she would receive such a great honor when, far away in Moab, she listened to Naomi telling those wonderful stories of the God of Israel, the God of heaven and earth. How glad she will be, through all eternity, that she gave her heart to Him then.

David the Lionhearted

(1 Samuel 17:1-53)

I T WAS lonesome around the house. Three of David's older brothers had gone to help Saul fight the Philistines. Father and Mother were worrying about what might happen to them on the battlefield.

David was worried too. Out there on the hillside, looking after the sheep, he kept thinking about Eliab, Abinadab, and Shammah. Perhaps they would be killed or taken prisoners, and he would never see them again. That made him sad.

As he lay on the soft green grass, with the sheep feeding around him and the cool wind blowing over him, he wondered why people had to fight and kill each other. Then he remembered how one day a lion had come to attack his sheep, and he had fought and killed it all by himself. Would he ever forget that lion, or the bear that had tried to make off with one of his lambs? He hadn't wanted to kill them, but there was no other way to protect the sheep.

The Philistines were different. They should have known better. Why didn't they stay in their own country? Why did they have to come and bother other people?

Suddenly from far away came a familiar call.

"David!"

It was Jesse, his father. He wanted to send some food to the boys in camp. Would David please take it?

Would he! There was nothing he wanted to do more. Perhaps he would be there in time to see the battle. Maybe he would get a good look at the Philistines and find out what sort of people they were.

"Early in the morning David left the flock with a shepherd, loaded up and set out, as Jesse had directed."

We don't know how far he had to travel, but at last he came to the camp. He left the food with the man in charge, then searched among the soldiers until he found his brothers.

He was glad to see them again! But Eliab, the oldest, didn't give him a very happy greeting. Angrily he asked why David had come, and what was happening to the sheep he had left behind. "I know how conceited you are," Eliab said, "and how wicked your heart is; you came down only to watch the battle."

"Now what have I done?" sighed David, like any boy who has been scolded by an older brother.

Just then someone shouted, "Look, there he comes!"

David looked. To his amazement, a giant of a man, at least nine feet tall, wearing a huge bronze helmet, a bronze coat of scale armor, and bronze armor on his legs, came out of the camp of the Philistines. "His spear was as thick as the bar on a weaver's loom, and its iron head weighed about fifteen pounds [7 kilograms]" (TEV).

"Who's that?" asked David.

"Goliath of Gath," said someone, beginning to run away as the giant strode down into the valley which separated the two armies.

Why is everybody running away? wondered David. Why doesn't somebody stand up to this giant?

Disappointed and angry, he said aloud, "Who is this un-circumcised Philistine that he should defy the armies of the living God?"

Somebody heard what he said and told King Saul, who sent for David.

"Let no one lose heart on account of this Philistine," David said to the king. "Your servant will go and fight him."

Saul wouldn't hear of it. "You can't go," he said. "You're too young."

But David told the king about his fight with the lion and the bear, adding, "The Lord who delivered me from the paw of the lion and the paw of the bear will deliver me from the hand of this Philistine."

At last King Saul was convinced. This was a boy with the heart of a lion and strong in the strength of God. He told David he could go and fight Goliath if he wanted to, and he gave him a suit of his own armor to protect him.

Of course, the armor was too big. Nothing fit. David felt uncomfortable. "I cannot go in these," he said, and took the armor all off again.

Then, with his staff in his hand, he walked down to the brook in the valley and carefully chose five smooth rocks, putting them in the shepherd's bag which he carried.

What in the world is he doing? everybody wondered as they watched him calmly picking up one rock after another and judging them for weight and shape and smoothness. Is he just going to throw stones at the man?

They wondered even more as they saw him walk toward the towering figure of the waiting Philistine with no weapon but a sling.

As David drew nearer, Goliath became very angry and cursed him by the Philistine gods. "Am I a dog," he cried, "that you come at me with sticks? . . . Come here, . . . and I'll give your flesh to the birds of the air and the beasts of the field!"

David didn't pay any attention to this threat. Without a trace of fear, he replied in never-to-be-forgotten words: "You come against me with sword and spear and javelin, but I come against you in the name of the Lord Almighty, the God of the armies of Israel, whom you have defied.

"This day the Lord will hand you over to me. . . . The whole world will know that there is a God in Israel. All those gathered here will know that it is not by sword or spear that the Lord saves; for the battle is the Lord's, and he will give all of you into our hands."

This was too much for Goliath. His face livid with anger, he lunged forward, his enormous spear grasped tightly in his massive hands.

Still David did not flinch. Instead, he calmly took one of the rocks from his bag, put it in his sling, and threw it with all his strength at the advancing giant. The watching thousands held their breath. Everyone knew there could be no second shot.

Suddenly Goliath stopped, stumbled, fell, his huge spear clattering to the ground. The rock had struck him in the forehead. Running toward the fallen Philistine, David grabbed the giant's sword and cut off his head.

The battle was as good as over. Seeing their champion dead, the rest of the Philistines fled in terror, the Israelites chasing them clear back to their own country.

How much God can do through one dear boy who loves and trusts Him with all his heart!

Four Noble Young Men

(Daniel 1)

WHERE am I?" asked Daniel, rubbing his eyes.

"Prison!" muttered Hananiah, who lay beside him in the dungeon. "We're in Babylon."

Babylon! Suddenly it all came back. What a nightmare! Daniel remembered how the prisoners had been seized and bound, the dreadful march across the desert to Babylon, the blows and curses of the conquerors, and finally prison.

Now, as the morning sun shone through the grating above their heads, Daniel, Hananiah, Mishael, and Azariah began to realize what a sad, sad thing had happened to them. All four belonged to good families in Judah. They had always enjoyed the best of everything. Now they had nothing, not even freedom.

As they looked ahead, the future seemed dark. They would never again see their beloved country, their homes, their fathers and mothers, their brothers and sisters. For the rest of their lives they would be slaves of a hated enemy.

← PAINTING BY RUSSELL HARLAN

Daniel and his companions purposed in their hearts not to be defiled with the dainties and wine offered to them from the king's table, and asked to be served only the plainest food.

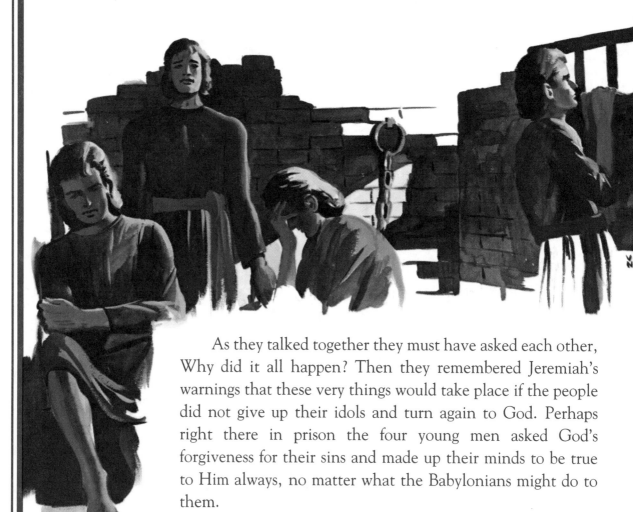

As they talked together they must have asked each other, Why did it all happen? Then they remembered Jeremiah's warnings that these very things would take place if the people did not give up their idols and turn again to God. Perhaps right there in prison the four young men asked God's forgiveness for their sins and made up their minds to be true to Him always, no matter what the Babylonians might do to them.

One day the prison door opened, and an officer named Ashpenaz came in. He looked over the prisoners and picked out Daniel, Hananiah, Mishael, and Azariah. At first they wondered why. Had they done something wrong?

Ashpenaz explained that Nebuchadnezzar was a great and farseeing king. He did not kill all his captives. Instead he chose the best of them, those who appeared strong, healthy, and intelligent, and he educated them in the schools of Babylon. In this way, they would become a strength to the country in days to come. The four boys, he said, should consider themselves very fortunate that they were among the few chosen for this honor.

They did. They were very happy about it. But they were worried about what else this honor might mean. Would they be expected to worship the gods of Babylon?

They were even more worried when Ashpenaz told them that their names would be changed. Now they would have Babylonian, not Hebrew, names. Daniel was given the name of Belteshazzar; Hananiah was called Shadrach; Mishael, Meshach; and Azariah, Abednego. Apparently their masters meant to change them completely. They were to forget they were Hebrews and become Babylonians.

Then came the first big test.

King Nebuchadnezzar gave orders that the captives who had been chosen to be taught "the language and literature of the Babylonians" should be fed from the king's table. They were to eat what he ate.

No doubt the king thought he was doing the captives a very great favor in providing them "a daily amount of food and wine from the king's table"—and he was. But Daniel and his friends were troubled. They felt they couldn't eat the food that was prepared for the king. It was probably first offered to idols. And much of it was forbidden by God as "unclean." As for the wine, it was the fermented kind that was full of alcohol, so they couldn't take that either.

What should they do? Was it worth fussing about? After all, it was only food and drink. Maybe they could take just a little and avoid offending the king. Surely when a heathen king had gone so far in trying to be kind and generous to his captives, it would be downright rude not to take the food and drink he gave them.

"But Daniel resolved not to defile himself with the royal food and wine." He felt that if he were to yield on this point, he would give away everything. He could never take a stand on anything else. If he was going to be loyal to God all the way, he had better start here and now.

So Daniel plucked up his courage and spoke to Ashpenaz. He respectfully explained why he and his three friends could not take the food so kindly offered them. Would it be all right if they had something else? Nothing special of course—just vegetables and cereals, and good plain water to drink.

Ashpenaz listened patiently. He liked this young man. Indeed, "God had caused the official to show favor and sympathy to Daniel." But now he was worried. He didn't see how it could be done.

"I am afraid of my lord the king," he said. "If you don't eat the food he has provided, and

you become thinner than the rest of the boys, he'll take my head off."

Daniel knew how easily this could happen. Yet he felt sure all would be well. So he went to Melzar, the guard Ashpenaz had put in charge of the four boys, and told him what they wanted to do. "Just let us try it for ten days," he pleaded. "Give us vegetables to eat and water to drink. Then look us over and do what seems best."

With many feelings of doubt, Melzar agreed. Instead of the king's food and wine, he gave them vegetables, cereals, and water. And you can imagine how he watched them day by day for the first signs of weakness!

But they didn't fall sick, and their faces didn't grow thin and pale as Melzar had expected. "At the end of the ten days they looked healthier and better nourished than any of the young men who ate the royal food."

Melzar was surprised and very pleased. From now on he gladly gave the four boys the food they wanted. And somehow they were able to think more clearly than the

others. They remembered their lessons better. Living on a clean, simple diet, they were able to gather knowledge and wisdom faster than all the rest put together.

At the end of three years they graduated from school with highest honors. As a special reward, they were presented to King Nebuchadnezzar. "The king talked with them."

They had never expected this! Certainly not on that far-off night when they arrived, all weary and discouraged, at the prison. As for Nebuchadnezzar, he was impressed. Of all the young men he had in training, "he found none equal to Daniel, Hananiah, Mishael and Azariah; so they entered the king's service. In every matter of wisdom and understanding about which the king questioned them, he found them ten times better than all the magicians and enchanters in his whole kingdom."

Would you like to be "ten times better" than all the boys and girls in your school? Ten times wiser, 10 times healthier, 10 times nobler? You can be. Just determine in your heart to serve God always, whatever the cost. 🍃

Night With the Lions

(Daniel 6)

WHEN the Medo-Persians took possession of Babylon, they found Daniel in his house but did not kill him. Instead, learning that he had just been made the third highest ruler of the kingdom, they took him before Darius.

It could well be that the new king had already heard of Daniel during the many years that this famous Hebrew slave was Nebuchadnezzar's prime minister. As they talked together Daniel made such a deep impression upon Darius that the king included him in his new government. When Darius appointed "120 satraps to rule throughout the kingdom," he appointed Daniel the first of three administrators in charge of them.

Unfortunately, the other two administrators and the 120 satraps did not like this plan. They thought it was unfair that anyone who had held an important position in Babylon should be put ahead of good, loyal Medo-Persians.

These jealous men did their best to get rid of Daniel. They spread wicked rumors about him, charging him with being a traitor and accusing him of one wrong thing after another. But they couldn't prove any of their charges.

Every time they tried to build a case against Daniel, it collapsed "because he was trustworthy and neither corrupt nor negligent." Daniel was so honest, so true, so loyal, that these men finally said to each other, "We will find nothing against him unless it has to do with his religion."

These men knew that Daniel never failed to say his prayers three times a day—morning, noon, and night. So they plotted together to persuade King Darius to issue a decree that no one could pray "to any god or man" except himself, for the next 30 days. The penalty for disobeying the decree would be death in the lions' den.

Darius, very flattered by the suggestion, signed the decree. Then someone came and told Daniel about the new law. He saw through the wicked scheme at once. But did he change his lifelong habit of daily worship? Did he decide to give up saying his prayers, or to whisper them secretly, out of sight? No, not he! He had witnessed for God all his life in this heathen city, and he was not going to give up now. If it meant dying in the lions' den, that's what he would do. He would be faithful unto death.

"When Daniel learned that the decree had been published, he went home to his upstairs room where the windows opened toward Jerusalem. Three times a day he got down on his knees and prayed, giving thanks to his God, just as he had done before."

People were used to seeing Daniel praying at that

window, but now they crowded the street in front of his house to witness his quiet defiance of the new law. "Look at him!" they cried. "Doesn't he know about the king's decree?"

"He'll know when he finds himself in the lions' den," said others.

Meanwhile, the jealous satraps hurried to Darius with the story. Too late, the king realized what they had led him to do. He was very angry, but having made the decree, there was nothing he could do but order that Daniel be thrown to the lions.

So Daniel was arrested and led through the streets to the den. What a procession that must have been! The aged prophet walked in front, followed by the satraps and many soldiers. Thousands of men and women, boys and girls, watched the group pass, many of them sad that this dear man was going to be killed. But Daniel strode on unmoved, his trust in God unshaken.

The door of the den was opened and Daniel was thrown in. But the lions did not touch him. Instead they slunk away, as though afraid of him. All that night, as Daniel prayed, the lions paced back and forth. They growled now and then but never tried to attack him.

Early in the morning Daniel heard a familiar voice calling

to him from outside the den. It was the king!

"Daniel, Daniel," cried Darius, "servant of the living God, has your God, whom you serve continually, been able to rescue you from the lions?"

Oh, yes, indeed. Well able.

"My God sent his angel," Daniel told the king, "and he shut the mouths of the lions. They have not hurt me."

"The king was overjoyed and gave orders to lift Daniel out of the den. And . . . no wound was found on him, because he had trusted in his God."

Some may say that the lions did not touch Daniel because they weren't hungry. Oh, but they were! When those who had found fault with Daniel were thrown into the lions' den themselves, there was a terrible scene. The lions pounced on them at once, breaking all their bones into pieces before they reached the bottom of the den.

King Darius was so impressed by what happened that night that he sent a special message to everybody in his kingdom, saying, "I issue a decree that in every part of my kingdom people must fear and reverence the God of Daniel.

"For he is the living God and he endures forever. . . .

"He rescues and he saves; he performs signs and wonders in the heavens and on the earth. He has rescued Daniel from the power of the lions."

This wonderful message comes down across the centuries to you and me. The God who lived in Daniel's day is just the same today. "He endures forever," and He still delivers and rescues those who trust in Him.

← PAINTING BY KREIGH COLLINS

Because Daniel continued to pray to the true God, whom he had worshiped all his life, he was thrown into a den of lions, but an angel protected him by shutting the lions' mouths.

A Star Is Born

(Esther 1:1-2:7)

IF YOU had lived in Susa, capital of Medo-Persia, a little less than 2,500 years ago, you might have happened to see a very sad little girl.

Her name was Hadassah, the Hebrew name for Myrtle. She was very pretty, but oh, so unhappy! You see, her father had been dead for some time, and now her mother had died too, and she was all alone in the world.

Of course, in those hard, cruel times it was nothing new for a little girl to be left an orphan, but that didn't help poor Hadassah. All she could think of was that she had nobody to love her, nobody that is, except maybe her big cousin Mordecai. He was much older than she was, and married, with a home of his own and a job at the royal palace. She might be able to stay with him, if he would let her and if he cared enough for her.

Fortunately Mordecai did care. Gladly he took poor little Hadassah into his home and adopted her as his own daughter. Then he gave her a Persian name, "Esther," which

Mordecai loved his little orphan cousin Hadassah and cared for her in his own home, not knowing that someday as the lovely Queen Esther she would deliver the Jews.

means "a star." You can recognize it in the word "asterisk," which is a printer's mark that looks like a little star, and in "aster," the lovely starlike flower. In Babylon the morning and evening stars were worshiped as gods under the name "Ishtar."

What a bright little star Esther proved to be! "Lovely in form and features," she was the light of Mordecai's home and the pride and joy of his heart. You can imagine how glad he was in the evenings, when he returned from the palace to find her waiting for him with open arms. And night after night you may be sure he told her the dear old stories of God's wonderful love for His people, and how He had watched over them, in good times and bad, for hundreds and hundreds of years.

So Esther grew up to love and honor God. She learned to pray to Him and trust Him and to find strength through faith in His goodness.

Mordecai was one of the many Jews who had chosen to stay in Medo-Persia rather than return to Jerusalem. While it is true that 50,000 went back with Zerubbabel, hundreds of thousands of others stayed behind. The Medes and Persians, under King Cyrus and King Darius, had been kind to them, letting them work and worship as they pleased. It was easier to stay than to return. Some, like Mordecai, Ezra, and Nehemiah, found good jobs in the palace and became friends of the king. Others, scattered all over the country, worked in one kind of business or another and took part in the life of the empire as though they belonged to it.

Exactly what Mordecai's duties were we are not told. The Bible says that he sat "at the king's gate," which may mean he was an official in the court who waited with other royal servants near the palace entrance to obey the king's orders.

One evening when Mordecai arrived home, he told an exciting story. There had been a lot of trouble in the palace. Queen Vashti had been deposed! At a wild drinking party the night before, King Xerxes had ordered her to come to the party so that his nobles could see her beauty—and she had refused. Yes, she had refused! She had actually disobeyed the king, an unheard-of thing in Persia, where a wife was supposed to do whatever she was told by her husband. In his anger Xerxes had said that Vashti was no longer queen. He wouldn't have her in the palace. She had to go. And she had gone.

It was quite a story, and everybody was telling it to everybody else all over the empire. I can hear little Esther saying, "But, dear Mordecai, what will the king do for a queen? He will have to have a queen, won't he?"

And Mordecai may well have said, "Yes, my dear, of course he will. He's probably looking for one now. Who knows? Perhaps he will want you to be his queen!"

"Oh no, he would never think of me," she said, laughing at her uncle's fun. "He'd never want a Jewish girl like me."

"You never can tell," said Mordecai. "Stranger things than that have happened. And what a lovely queen you would make, my little star!"

Orphan Girl Becomes Queen

(Esther 2:2-17)

THERE must have been a lot of excitement in Persia those days. Every girl from India to Cush, in all the 127 provinces of the empire, was talking about the king's search for a new queen. Everyone hoped she would be the one to be chosen. And you may be sure that every mother was certain her daughter was the most worthy for this high honor.

By the king's command, beauty contests, or something similar, were held in every province, and the loveliest girls were given a free trip to Susa for the king's inspection.

As more and more girls arrived at the palace, Mordecai had an idea. Why, his Esther was far more beautiful than any of these young ladies from Aram, Egypt, Arabia, and other parts of the country. They didn't stand a chance beside his precious little star. They weren't in the same class. Esther was far and away the best-looking girl in the world.

"I'm sure you could win," he told her one day, after seeing some of the latest arrivals. "You're so much lovelier than any of the others. Why not try and see what happens? It could be that God wants you to be queen."

Finally Esther agreed, and she "was taken to the king's palace and entrusted to Hegai, who had charge of the harem." As Mordecai told her goodbye, he added one word of caution. "Don't tell anyone you are a Jewess," he said. "That might spoil everything."

"I won't," said Esther, and she was gone.

When Hegai saw Esther, he was so struck with her beauty that he felt sure she would be chosen queen. So he gave her the best rooms in the house of the women and seven maids to wait on her.

This was encouraging, but it didn't mean that Esther *would* be queen. After all, the king had to see all the other girls before he could make up his mind; and there might be someone else prettier than she.

As for poor Mordecai, he waited impatiently for news about his precious daughter. He felt certain that the king would choose her. How could he do otherwise? But if he didn't, what would happen to her? Would she be allowed to come home again?

"Every day he walked back and forth near the courtyard of the harem to find out how Esther was and what was happening to her." Can't you see him pacing back and forth, looking up at the barred windows, hoping to get a glimpse of her face or a wave of her hand?

"O Esther, Esther, where are you?" I can hear him calling. "What has happened to you, my little star?"

Twelve months passed. Then one day Esther was called to meet the king. How excited she must have been! How hard she must have tried to look her very best! How she must have prayed for God's help and guidance on this greatest day of her life!

Mordecai was waiting outside, you can be sure. And when Esther walked from the women's house to meet the king, dressed in the finest robes the Persian court could supply and attended by all her lovely maidens, I can imagine he almost burst with pride. Such a beautiful dream she was! Onlookers in the corridors gasped in wonder as she passed by. Indeed she "won the favor of everyone who saw her."

At last she came into "the royal residence," and the king was overcome by her breathtaking beauty. It was a case of love at first sight. "Now the king was attracted to Esther more than to any of the other women, and she won his favor and approval more than any of the other virgins. So he set a royal crown on her head and made her queen."

Plots in the Palace

(Esther 2:21-23; 3)

NO KING was very safe on his throne in those days. Someone or another was always plotting to take his life.

The famous Xerxes was no exception. Soon after Esther became his queen, two of his chamberlains, Bigthana and Teresh, became so angry at something he had done that they made up their minds to kill him.

Unfortunately for them, they talked about their plan to others, who whispered it to their friends, who whispered it to *their* friends, and so on, until finally the story reached Mordecai. He told Esther, and Esther told the king. The two plotters were arrested and put to death. But in all the excitement, Mordecai was forgotten. The king did not even thank him for his help.

About this time Xerxes chose a man named Haman the Agagite to be his prime minister. He probably was a descendant of Agag, king of Amalek, whom the prophet Samuel killed.

It was not a good choice. Haman may have been strong,

but he was also proud, cruel, and ruthless. Mordecai did not like him and could not bring himself to bow to him as the law required. When Haman came striding through the servants' quarters near the palace gate, everybody paid him deep respect—everybody, that is, except Mordecai. He just looked the other way.

Day after day this went on, and soon all the king's servants were talking about it. "You'll get into trouble," some of them said to Mordecai. "It's the king's orders that everybody bow to Haman. You'd better do it."

"Not I," said Mordecai. "I couldn't. Not to him."

And he didn't. This made Haman terribly angry. The sight of that one man standing erect when all the rest were bowing to him was more than he could endure.

About this time he learned that Mordecai was a Jew, and this gave him an idea. He would take his revenge not only on

Mordecai but on all the Jews. He would wipe them off the face of the earth.

To make quite sure that his plot would succeed, he went to the priests of his heathen gods and had them cast lots to find the best time to purge the Jews from the Persian Empire. The lot fell on the thirteenth day of the twelfth month.

Then he went to King Xerxes and outlined his plan, making the king believe, of course, that his idea was in the best interests of king and country.

"There is a certain people dispersed and scattered among the peoples in all the provinces of your kingdom," he said, "whose customs are different from those of all other people and who do not obey the king's laws; it is not in the king's best interest to tolerate them. If it pleases the king, let a decree be issued to destroy them."

So that the king wouldn't object that such a large job might cost too much money, Haman offered to pay all the expenses himself. "I will put ten thousand talents [375 tons, or 345 metric tonnes] of silver into the royal treasury for the men who

carry out this business," he said.

The king's confidence in Haman was so great that he told him to do as he pleased. "Here, take my ring," he said; "write your own decree and sign it in my name."

Haman was delighted. Things were going better than he had dared to hope. He chuckled when he thought of what he would do to Mordecai in just a little while.

Calling the king's scribes, he had them prepare the decree, which was then sent to all the governors of the 127 provinces. It ordered them "to destroy, kill and annihilate all the Jews—young and old, women and little children—on a single day, the thirteenth day of the twelfth month, . . . and to plunder their goods."

It was a terrible thing to do. It meant the massacre of the entire Jewish race. It was worse than anything Pharaoh had tried to do in Egypt. But what did Haman care? When the decree had been read in Susa, he and the king "sat down to drink."

But they had forgotten something. They had failed to reckon with the God of Israel, who has a special concern for His people. They had also overlooked the fact that He had a bright little star shining in the palace at that very moment.

Esther's Grand Decision

(Esther 4)

YOU CAN imagine how Mordecai felt when he heard about the king's decree. The Bible says that he "tore his clothes, put on sackcloth and ashes, and went out into the city, wailing loudly and bitterly."

All over Medo-Persia, wherever the decree was read, there were similar scenes of sorrow. In every city and village "there was great mourning among the Jews, with fasting, weeping and wailing. Many lay in sackcloth and ashes."

When Esther's maids told her how upset Mordecai was, she wondered what could be the matter. She sent him some new clothes to cheer him up, but he would not accept them. She guessed then that something serious must be wrong and sent her most trusted servant to find out what it was.

"Mordecai told him everything that had happened . . . , including the exact amount of money Haman had promised to pay into the royal treasury for the destruction of the Jews. He also gave him a copy of the text of the edict . . . , to show to Esther."

Mordecai begged Esther to go and see the king and persuade him to change his mind, but Esther told him through her messenger that she couldn't possibly do that. No one, not even the queen herself, was allowed to go to the king unless specially invited. It was a law, and death was the penalty for disobedience.

Mordecai replied, "Don't think you will escape." Then he added, in words that will live forever, "For if you remain silent at this time, relief and deliverance for the Jews will arise from another place, but you and your father's family will perish. And *who knows but that you have come to royal position for such a time as this?*"

Esther's heart was touched. Suddenly she understood why she, a little orphan girl, had been made queen. God had planned it! He knew this terrible crisis was coming and He had made her queen to save His people. She had indeed come to the kingdom for such a time as this.

But how could she go to the king? It was as much as her life was worth. Yet if God wanted her to do it, she would go, trusting in His protection.

She sent this message back to Mordecai: "Go, gather together all the Jews who are in Susa, and fast for me. Do not eat or drink for three days, night or day. I and my maids will fast as you do. When this is done, I will go to the king, even though it is against the law. And if I perish, I perish."

Brave Esther! Noble little star! What a grand decision she made!

How the Jews must have prayed for her during those next few days! Never had the synagogues of Susa been so crowded with solemn-faced people, all pleading with God to watch over their dear, beautiful queen and to help her bring deliverance to her people.

In every Jewish home throughout the city, boys and girls prayed also, for they knew very well that their lives were in danger too. "Bless dear Queen Esther," I can hear them saying. "Keep her safe. Help her to be brave. Don't let any harm come to her. Make the king be nice to her. And don't let him kill us all." The prayers from young and old went heavenward, while angels drew near to help.

And the face of God's little star shone brighter than ever as she plucked up her courage to go in to see the king.

Royal Invitation

(Esther 5)

ALL THE next day and the day after, Esther thought about what she should do. If she went to see the king, would he welcome her? And if he did, what would she say to him? How could she possibly persuade him to change his mind and rewrite the decree? Persian kings never altered their decrees. It wasn't done.

Then too, Xerxes might be in a bad mood. He might be angry with her for coming to see him. He might have her put in prison or executed. It was a terrible risk to take.

Then she had a bright idea. Calling her maids, she told them to prepare a very special banquet at her house. Then, putting on her royal robes and looking more beautiful than ever, she made her way slowly to the king's house.

When she reached the entrance of the great hall where Xerxes was seated on his royal throne, she placed herself where he could see her. Would he hold out his golden scepter to her as a token of welcome? He did. Catching sight of his

lovely young queen, he smiled at her and asked her to come close to him.

As Esther touched the top of his golden scepter, he asked what he could do for her. Graciously he offered to give her anything she wanted, even if it was half of his kingdom. Probably he didn't mean exactly that, but it sounded nice and was a custom in those days.

Esther was ready. She had made up her mind to make a very simple request at first—one that the king would surely agree to. She would just invite him to dinner.

"If it pleases the king," she said very sweetly, "let the king, together with Haman, come today to a banquet I have prepared for him."

"Of course, of course!" said the king, no doubt relieved that she wanted so little of him and flattered at this mark of her approval of his prime minister. At once he sent a messenger to tell Haman to hurry up and do as the queen had asked.

Haman was overjoyed. This was the greatest reward he had ever received. To have dinner alone with the king and queen was an honor he had never dared to hope for.

That evening the two men came to Esther's apartment, where everything was beautifully prepared for them. They ate and drank happily together; then the king asked again, "What do you want, Esther? There must be something."

"There is," said Esther, with all her charm. "My request is

← PAINTING BY HERBERT RUDEEN

When the king held forth the golden scepter to show that she was welcome in the court, Queen Esther touched it, and asked the king and Haman to be her guests at a royal dinner.

that you will both come to dinner again tomorrow. Then I will tell you."

Gladly the king agreed, but his curiosity was even more aroused. What could the queen want? Clearly she had something important on her mind. What was it? He must find out.

As for Haman, he had never been so happy in his life. Hurrying home, he called his wife Zeresh and his closest friends and told them about his good fortune. In his excitement he told about all "his vast wealth" and how the king had promoted him above all his nobles and officials.

"And now, just think," he added, "the queen has invited me to have dinner with her and the king twice in two days! I'd be the happiest man in the world if it weren't for that Mordecai.

He's the only man in the palace who refuses to bow when I pass by. He makes me so angry I can hardly contain myself."

"Why bother about him?" said Zeresh. "Why let one old Jew spoil your happiness? Get him out of the way."

"Good idea!" said his friends. "Have a gallows made, the highest ever built in Susa. Then when you meet the king tomorrow, ask him to let you hang Mordecai on it. If he agrees, you can forget your troubles and go merrily to the banquet."

"This suggestion delighted Haman, and he had the gallows built." It was 75 feet high—high enough so all the city could see his hated enemy dangling from it.

But he built it a little too soon.

The Biter Is Bitten

(Esther 6; 7)

THAT night the king could not sleep. Maybe he was still thinking about Esther's banquet or worrying about what was on her mind. Anyhow, sleep would not come. So he sent for the book of the chronicles and told a servant to read from it.

Now it so happened that the chapter the servant read was all about the two traitors, Bigthana and Teresh, who had tried to murder the king, and how Mordecai had discovered their plot just in time.

"What has been done for this man Mordecai?" asked the king.

"Nothing so far," said the servant.

Just then Haman entered the room, wanting to ask the king's permission to hang Mordecai.

Catching sight of him, the king said, "Haman, what should be done for the man whom the king delights to honor?"

Thinking that the king must be planning some further

promotion for him, Haman replied, "Let him be dressed in the king's robes, with a royal crest on his head; and let him ride through the city on the king's horse, with one of the most noble princes running before him crying, 'This is what is done for the man the king delights to honor!' "

"Good," said the king. "Now do just that to Mordecai the Jew."

"Mordecai!" gasped Haman. "Not Mordecai!"

But he dared not disobey.

So the king's robes, a royal crest, and the royal horse were prepared as though Xerxes himself were going to use them. Then Mordecai was dressed up as the king of Persia.

Surely he must have been the most surprised man in Susa

that day. And how all the nobles and the officials, and even the king himself must have laughed as they saw Haman running ahead of Mordecai through the palace gates crying, "This is what is done for the man the king delights to honor!"

As the strange procession passed along the city streets, thousands of men and women, boys and girls, gaped in wonder.

"Surely it can't be Haman," I can hear them saying. "Not the prime minister himself, running before Mordecai the Jew!"

Before nightfall all Susa must have been rocking with laughter. Mordecai must have been amused too, but Haman was crushed. It was more than he could take. Hurrying home, he told Zeresh, his wife, and his friends about how humiliated he felt.

He must have been tired, too, after such a long run, but he had no time to rest. While he was still telling the story the king's eunuchs arrived to lead him in state to Esther's banquet.

How he had looked forward to this occasion! Now he didn't care whether he went or not. Would the king tease him about what had happened that afternoon? What would the queen say, if she had heard of it? And how could he ask the king to hang Mordecai now?

The banquet began. Richly dressed servants waited on the king and queen and Haman. The most delicate foods which the palace cooks could provide were spread on the table.

It wasn't long before the king, unable to hold back his curiosity, asked, "What is your petition, Esther? What do you want of me?"

"I ask my life and the life of my people," she said boldly, but pleadingly. "For I and my people have been sold for destruction and slaughter and annihilation."

"Who is there in my kingdom who would dare to think of such a thing?" asked the king in great surprise.

"Haman," said the queen. "This vile Haman."

White with anger, the king rose from his seat and strode out into the palace garden, leaving Haman alone with the queen.

Sensing his danger, Haman began to plead for Esther's forgiveness. He wanted her to beg the king not to have him put to death. In a frenzy of fear he flung himself on the couch where she was resting, just as the king came back into the banqueting hall.

Thinking Haman planned to harm the queen, the king became more furious than ever. As the servants dragged Haman out of the banquet hall, one of the eunuchs told the king about the gallows Haman had built for Mordecai.

"Hang him on it!" cried the king.

"So they hanged Haman on the gallows he had prepared for Mordecai."

This, then, is what happened to the man who plotted to kill all the children of Israel in one day. And so Haman, the biter, was bitten.

FOR SCHOOL-AGE CHILDREN
The Bible Story
This is the most accurate and complete set of children's Bible story books available. More than 400 Bible stories are included, with full color paintings at every page-opening. Unlike television, these stories introduce children to heroes you would be proud to have them imitate. These stories are also an excellent tool for loving parents who want their children to grow up making right decisions and making them with confidence. Ten volumes, hardcover.

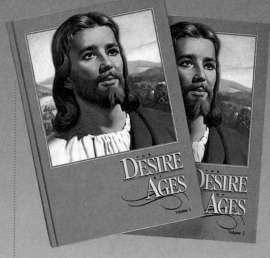

The Desire of Ages
This is E. G. White's monumental best-seller on the life of Christ. It is perhaps the most spiritually perceptive of the Saviour's biographies since the Gospel According to John. Here Jesus becomes more than a historic figure—He is the great divine-human personality set forth in a hostile world to make peace between God and man. Two volumes, hardcover.

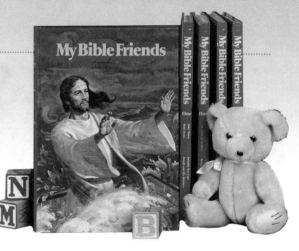

Uncle Arthur's Bedtime Stories
For years this collection of stories has been the center of cozy reading experiences between parents and children. Arthur Maxwell tells the real-life adventures of young children—adventures that teach the importance of character traits like kindness and honesty. Discover how a hollow pie taught Robert not to be greedy and how an apple pie shared by Annie saved her life. Five volumes, hardcover.

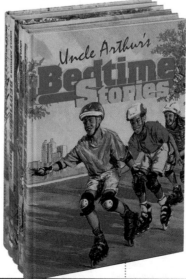

FOR PRESCHOOL CHILDREN
My Bible Friends
Imagine your child's delight as you read the charming story of Small Donkey, who carried tired Mary up the hill toward Bethlehem. Or of Zacchaeus the Cheater, who climbed a sycamore tree so he could see Jesus passing by. Each book has four attention-holding stories written in simple, crystal-clear language. And the colorful illustrations surpass in quality what you may have seen in any other children's Bible story book. Five volumes, hardcover. Also available in videos and audio cassettes.

For more information, write: The Bible Story, P.O. Box 1119, Hagerstown, MD 21741.

MORE *FAMILY* READING

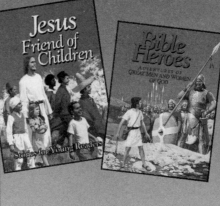

God's Answers to Your Questions
You ask the questions; it points you to Bible texts with the answers

He Taught Love
The true meaning hidden within the parables of Jesus

Jesus, Friend of Children
Favorite chapters from *The Bible Story*

Bible Heroes
A selection of the most exciting adventures from *The Bible Story*

The Storybook
Excerpts from Uncle Arthur's *Bedtime Stories*

My Friend Jesus
Stories for preschoolers from the life of Christ, with activity pages

Foods That Heal
Nutrition expert explains how to change your life by improving your diet

Plants That Heal
Unlocks the secrets of plants that heal the body and invigorate the mind

Choices: Quick and Healthy Cooking
Healthy meal plans you can make in a hurry

More Choices for a Healthy, Low-Fat You
All-natural meals you can make in 30 minutes

Tasty Vegan Delights
Exceptional recipes without animal fats or dairy products

Fun With Kids in the Kitchen Cookbook
Let your kids help with these healthy recipes

Health Power
Choices you can make that will revolutionize your health

Secret Keys
Character-building stories for children

Joy in the Morning
Replace disappointment and despair with inner peace and lasting joy

FOR MORE INFORMATION:
- **mail** the attached card
- or **write**
  Home Health Education Service
  P.O. Box 1119
  Hagerstown, MD 21741
- or **visit** www.thebiblestory.com